EDWARD LEAR'S
BOOK OF NONSENSE

There was an Old Derry down Derry,
Who loved to see little folks merry;
So he made them a book,
And with laughter they shook,
At the fun of that Derry down Derry.

EDWARD LEAR'S
BOOK OF NONSENSE

SPRING
BOOKS

This edition first published in Great Britain in 1980 by
J.M. Dent & Sons Ltd.

Published in 1988 by Spring Books
An imprint of Octopus Publishing Group PLC
59 Grosvenor Street
London W1

Distributed by The Hamlyn Publishing Group Limited
Bridge House, London Road,
Twickenham, Middlesex, England

ISBN 0 600 55918 1

Printed by Mandarin Offset in Hong Kong

EDWARD LEAR'S BOOK OF NONSENSE

In 1866, twenty years after his bestselling *Book of Nonsense* was first published, Edward Lear was sitting in a railway carriage beside two ladies whose children were gleefully reading it out loud. Also present was an elderly gentleman who, like the ladies was unaware of Lear's identity and reliably informed them that the book's author was actually Edward, Earl of Derby, explaining that LEAR was simply an anagram of EARL. *"There is no such person as Edward Lear"*, he assured them. At this point Lear, silent until now, declared that he was indeed Edward Lear, the author of *A Book of Nonsense*, producing such irrefutable evidence as his name inside his hat, several letters and a monogrammed handkerchief. Like the characters in many of his limericks his travelling companions were left open-mouthed in astonishment.

Edward Lear was born on 12 May 1812 – the same year as Charles Dickens – in Holloway, then a fashionable village in North London. He was one of twenty-one children of a stockbroker after the failure of whose business the family dispersed. Edward lived for a time with his older sister, Ann, and saw very little of his parents. He had virtually no education but was a classic Victorian polymath who taught himself several languages, was an accomplished musician and, in particular, a highly talented artist. He began by making anatomical sketches for doctors – a traditional study aid until it was replaced by photography – but soon started to specialize in animal subjects. His finest work was his beautiful series of hand-coloured lithographs of parrots published from 1830–32. Now greatly prized by collectors, they are among the most magnificent bird pictures ever produced and were an exceptional achievement for an unknown artist, not yet twenty, without formal art training and working in a relatively new and demanding medium. One of the subscribers to his *Illustrations of the Family of Psittacidae, or Parrots*, was Lord Stanley, heir to Lord Derby's title, who invited him to stay at the family seat, Knowsley Hall near Manchester, to draw the animals in his large private zoo.

Edward Lear proves his identity to the disbelieving man in the train.

Lear worked at Knowsley on and off for nearly five years, but eventually embarked on a series of extensive travels through Europe, the Holy Land and later to India. He kept detailed illustrated travel journals which were published at intervals, and supported himself on the income derived from these, from sales of landscape paintings and gifts and loans from several wealthy patrons. His renowned abilities as a 'topographical landscape painter' led in 1846 to his being invited to give drawing lessons to Queen Victoria. As he caricatured himself, with advancing years Lear grew rotund, shaggily bearded and increasingly short-sighted. His innate shyness prevented him from ever proposing marriage, although he came close to doing so on at least two occasions. He once wrote, "Every marriage of people I care about seems to leave me on the bleak shore alone – naturally." But he had many friends, both women and men, including the Tennyson family and the Pre-Raphaelite painter, William Holman Hunt. During his half-century of travels he wrote letters to them containing 'nonsense' in the form of humorous sketches and made-up words. Apart from his *Book of Nonsense*, many of his other poems, stories and drawings were published during and after his lifetime, perhaps his best known poem being *The Owl and the Pussycat*. He remained almost permanently out of England after 1837, travelling, writing, drawing and painting. He made his permanent home in San Remo, Italy, where he died on 29 January 1888.

Lear's early years had been dogged not only by domestic strife but also by ill-health, including a type of epilepsy which tormented him physically and isolated him socially. He was tall and lanky, with

a large nose, and felt awkward in adult company. However, at Knowsley he became friendly with the numerous children of the household for whom he drew comical sketches of animals and caricatures of people in a style quite unlike – and perhaps a welcome break from – his meticulously detailed natural history and landscape works. He accompanied these quick pen-and-ink drawings with rhymes in the form of limericks, a verse-form that had appeared in the 1820s. Prior to the publication of *A Book of Nonsense* most juvenile books presented educational, religious or moral lessons. Lear's limericks and illustrations were composed solely to entertain, and this novel aim and the originality of his nonsense made them immediately appealing to children.

No-one knows why, over a decade after producing them, Lear should have decided to attempt to reach a wider audience than the Knowsley children, but in 1845 he approached Thomas McClean, the printseller in London's Haymarket who had previously issued his *Views of Rome* (1844), with a view to having them published. They were printed by tracing the drawings and transferring them to specially prepared lithographic stone. Lear's verses, written in his erratic scrawl in the originals, were added by the printer in three lines of block capitals, written by hand onto the stone. In the printed version just one of his illustrations (featuring the 'Old Man of Leghorn') retained his initials; otherwise there was no mention of his name anywhere – maybe because he feared that its publication might harm his growing reputation as a serious artist. The book was

published on 10 February 1846, in two landscape volumes, about the same size as this book, selling for three shillings and sixpence each and containing a total of seventy-two limericks and illustrations. The first edition, now exceedingly rare, sold reasonably well and in 1854 a second edition was published in which the verses appeared in five lines printed in italics. About 1860 Lear decided to add extra limericks, bringing the total up to 112. He was probably never satisfied with the scratchy quality or the expense of printing them by lithography, and he therefore approached the brothers George and Edward Dalziel, who had founded the Camden Press in 1857 and who were regarded as two of the leading wood engravers of the Victorian era. They completely re-engraved the illustrations onto wood and printed them with the text set in Bodoni typeface (the same type used in this book) in the earlier three-line form. Lear offered the copyright in the book for £100 to the publishing company of Routledge, Warne and Routledge, who published many illustrated children's books. They declined, but entered a distribution arrangement, publishing the enlarged edition – and the first to bear Lear's name as author – in 1861. It sold out very quickly, and they then agreed to buy the rights to it, but Lear informed them that now it was a proven success they must pay more than the earlier asking price. A sum of £125 was agreed, and this, along with the modest profits he made from the previous editions, was all that Lear was to earn from a book which ran to 25 editions in his lifetime and which has now been continuously in print in various editions for over 130 years. The critical response was mixed. Lear was particularly annoyed to see it described as a "a reprint of old nursery rhymes", and remarked, "I wish someone would review it properly and funnily."

In 1865 the partnership of Routledge and Warne broke up and each established an independent company. The new firm founded by Frederick Warne in Covent Garden acquired the *Book of Nonsense* copyright, publishing the seventeenth edition in 1866. For the Christmas season of 1870 they had the Dalziels produce a giftbook version, also printed from woodblocks, in five colours and black and selling for five shillings, or in six parts at one shilling each, while the black and white version remained in print at three shillings and sixpence. Only 5,000 copies were printed, and it is from this now rare coloured edition that the following selection of illustrations has been made. In the United States, W. P. Hazard of Philadelphia published several uncoloured editions of the book in the 1860s, and after 1870 James Miller of New York, using Hazard's blocks, issued a coloured version as a rival to the Warne edition, available in America under an agreement with Scribner, Welford and Armstrong. Neither coloured edition remained in print, perhaps because colour plates were regarded as an expensive luxury better suited to the more detailed nursery illustrations of such artists as Kate Greenaway.

The first of the 'proper' reviews Lear craved came in the magazine, *Once a Week* (5 January 1867), which stated, "Never was a book published that so exactly hit the child's mind as this one." Among the features that made it so successful are the abandoned gaiety of the figures who are often depicted dancing or flinging themselves around ecstatically, and their frequent opposition to convention and authority – 'they', who appear as a disapproving force in many of the limericks, are symbols of the sort of killjoy orthodoxy that Lear is known to have abhorred. Lear's characters are almost invariably an 'Old Man' or an 'Old Person' who usually defies or amazes his fellows by performing some eccentric action – for which 'they' sometimes punish him. There are numerous references in the verses to those places that Lear visited, and some of the illustrations are derived from sketches executed on his travels. Many feature those animals and particularly birds which figured in his early artistic life, and some of his humans take on extraordinarily birdlike appearances. Fat, bearded and short-sighted men, and people with huge noses, all reflect Lear's abilities at self-caricature. Some of the limericks contain the sort of nonsense words, such as 'borascible' and 'scroobious', that he invented in his voluminous correspondence. Certain of his characters lose their fingers, or are even killed – or just saved from death – but they avoid being cruel or macabre by the total absurdity of the occurrence or through the quiet

Self-caricature of Edward Lear dancing.

reserve with which they greet their fate. They are thus no more shocking to a child than those modern children's cartoon characters who can be smashed to pieces but are always easily restored.

In 1886, two years before Lear's death, the eminent critic, John Ruskin, wrote an article in the *Pall Mall Magazine* in which he listed his hundred favourite authors. Describing the *Book of Nonsense* as, " . . . the most beneficent and innocent of all books yet produced", he wrote, "I really don't know of any author to whom I am half so grateful for my idle self as Edward Lear. I shall put him first of my hundred authors."

Edward Lear's *Book of Nonsense* predated Lewis Carroll's *Alice in Wonderland* by nearly twenty years and began a vogue for nonsense which persists in children's literature to the present day. He came to be prouder of it than any of his innumerable creations, especially when he saw the joy it gave to the children he loved – perhaps in compensation for his own lost childhood. The 'Old Derry down Derry' of the titlepage was Lear himself, a man 'who loved to see little folks merry', and whose lasting achievement is that, almost a century and a half after it was created, children continue to be amused by his *Book of Nonsense*.

RUSSELL ASH

There was an Old Person of Anerley,
Whose conduct was strange and unmannerly;
    He rushed down the Strand,
    With a Pig in each hand,
But returned in the evening to Anerley.

There was an Old Man with an Owl,
Who continued to bother and howl;
  He sat on a rail,
    And imbibed bitter ale,
Which refreshed that Old Man and his Owl.

There was an Old Man of the East,
Who gave all his children a feast;
    But they all ate so much,
    And their conduct was such,
That it killed that Old Man of the East.

There was an Old Person of Basing,
Whose presence of mind was amazing;
    He purchased a steed,
    Which he rode at full speed,
And escaped from the people of Basing.

There was an Old Person of Ems,
Who casually fell in the Thames;
  And when he was found,
  They said he was drowned,
That unlucky Old Person of Ems.

There was an Old Man at a casement,
Who held up his hands in amazement;
    When they said, "Sir! you'll fall!"
    He replied, "Not at all!"
That incipient Old Man at a casement.

There was an Old Man of Calcutta,
Who perpetually ate bread and butter;
　Till a great bit of muffin,
　On which he was stuffing,
Choked that horrid Old Man of Calcutta.

There was an Old Person of Tring,
Who embellished his nose with a ring;
   He gazed at the moon,
    Every evening in June,
That ecstatic Old Person of Tring.

There was an Old Man of Coblenz,
The length of whose legs was immense;
   He went with one prance,
   From Turkey to France,
That surprising Old Man of Coblenz.

There was an Old Man of Apulia,
Whose conduct was very peculiar:
   He fed twenty sons,
    Upon nothing but buns,
That whimsical Man of Apulia.

There was a Young Lady of Bute,
Who played on a silver-gilt flute;
    She played several jigs,
    To her uncle's white pigs,
That amusing Young Lady of Bute.

There was an Old Person of Mold,
Who shrank from sensations of cold;
  So he purchased some muffs,
  Some furs and some fluffs,
And wrapped himself well from the cold.

19

There was an Old Person of Bangor,
Whose face was distorted with anger;
    He tore off his boots,
    And subsisted on roots,
That borascible Person of Bangor.

There was an Old Man of Corfu,
Who never knew what he should do;
    So he rushed up and down,
    Till the sun made him brown,
That bewildered Old Man of Corfu.

There was an Old Person of Dover,
Who rushed through a field of blue clover;
    But some very large Bees,
    Stung his nose and his knees,
So he very soon went back to Dover.

There was an Old Man of Leghorn,
The smallest that ever was born;
   But quickly snapt up he,
   Was once by a Puppy,
Who devoured that Old Man of Leghorn.

There was a Young Person of Smyrna,
Whose grandmother threatened to burn her;
　　But she seized on the Cat,
　　And said, "Granny, burn that!
You incongruous Old Woman of Smyrna!"

There was an Old Man who said, "Hush!
I perceive a young bird in this bush!"
  When they said, "Is it small?"
  He replied, "Not at all!
It is four times as big as the bush!"

There was an Old Man with a flute,
A sarpint ran into his boot;
  But he played day and night,
  Till the sarpint took flight,
And avoided that Man with a flute.

There was an Old Person of Sparta,
Who had twenty-five sons and one daughter;
   He fed them on snails,
    And weighed them in scales,
That wonderful Person of Sparta.

There was an Old Man of Whitehaven,
Who danced a quadrille with a Raven;
    But they said, "It's absurd,
    To encourage this bird!"
So they smashed that Old Man of Whitehaven.

There was an Old Person of Tartary,
Who divided his jugular artery;
    But he screeched to his wife,
    And she said, "Oh, my life!
Your death will be felt by all Tartary!"

There was a Young Lady whose eyes,
Were unique as to colour and size;
    When she opened them wide,
    People all turned aside,
And started away in surprise.

There was an Old Man who supposed,
That the street door was partially closed;
   But some very large rats,
   Ate his coats and his hats,
While that futile old gentleman dozed.

There was a Young Lady of Dorking,
  Who bought a large bonnet for walking;
    But its colour and size,
    So bedazzled her eyes,
That she very soon went back to Dorking.

There was an Old Man of the Nile,
Who sharpened his nails with a file;
Till he cut off his thumbs,
And said calmly, "This comes—
Of sharpening one's nails with a file!"

There was an Old Person of Philae,
Whose conduct was scroobious and wily;
   He rushed up a Palm,
   When the weather was calm,
And observed all the ruins of Philae.

There was an Old Person of Cheadle,
Who was put in the stocks by the beadle;
  For stealing some pigs,
  Some coats and some wigs,
That horrible Person of Cheadle.

There was an Old Man with a beard,
Who said, "It is just as I feared!—
    Two Owls and a Hen,
    Four Larks and a Wren,
Have all built their nests in my beard!"

There was an Old Man of Melrose,
Who walked on the tips of his toes;
   But they said, "It ain't pleasant,
   To see you at present,
You stupid Old Man of Melrose."

There was an Old Man of the Hague,
Whose ideas were excessively vague;
   He built a balloon,
   To examine the moon,
That deluded Old Man of the Hague.

There was an Old Man in a pew,
Whose waistcoat was spotted with blue;
But he tore it in pieces,
To give to his nieces,—
That cheerful Old Man in a pew.

There was an Old Man on whose nose,
Most birds of the air could repose;
   But they all flew away,
   At the closing of day,
Which relieved that Old Man and his nose.

There was an Old Person of Dutton,
Whose head was as small as a button;
   So to make it look big,
   He purchased a wig,
And rapidly rushed about Dutton.

There was an Old Person whose habits,
Induced him to feed upon Rabbits;
   When he'd eaten eighteen,
   He turned perfectly green,
Upon which he relinquished those habits.

There was an Old Man of the North,
Who fell into a basin of broth;
  But a laudable cook,
  Fished him out with a hook,
Which saved that Old Man of the North.

There was a Young Lady of Portugal,
Whose ideas were excessively nautical;
    She climbed up a tree,
    To examine the sea,
But declared she would never leave Portugal.

There was an Old Man of the Cape,
Who possessed a large Barbary Ape;
   Till the Ape one dark night,
   Set the house all alight,
Which burned that Old Man of the Cape.

There was an Old Person of Rhodes,
Who strongly objected to toads;
    He paid several cousins,
    To catch them by dozens,
That futile Old Person of Rhodes.

There was an Old Man of the South,
Who had an immoderate mouth;
    But in swallowing a dish,
    That was quite full of fish,
He was choked, that Old Man of the South.

The End